The Faithful Daughter Shim Ch'ong

마음씨 고운 심청

The Little Frog Who Never Listened

말 안듣는 청개구리

HOLLYM

The Faithful Daughter Shim Ch'ong

A long time ago, in the land by the Yellow Sea, there lived a goodhearted girl named Shim Ch'ong. She was raised by her blind father because her mother died three days after she was born.

Blind Shim carried his little daughter from house to house in search of women to give her milk.

In spite of all the hardships, Ch'ong grew into a strong, healthy girl.

마음씨 고운 심 청

옛날, 황해도 땅에 심 청이라는 아이가 살고 있었습니다.

태어난지, 사흘만에 어머니가 돌아가신 불쌍한 청이는 앞 못 보는 아버지 손에 자랐습니다.

청이의 아버지 심 봉사는 어린 청이를 이집 저집 안고 다니며 젖을 얻어 먹여 키웠습니다.

그렇지만 청이는 아무 탈없이 무럭무럭 자랐습니다.

Because Blind Shim was unable to work, Ch'ong had to do odd jobs in other people's homes from an early age so that she could get food to feed her father.

Ch'ong was not only strong and healthy. She was also a very diligent worker. Everyone in the village praised her skill. Housewives even argued with each other over who would be next to get her to sew for them.

From morning until night, Ch'ong worked very hard for others so that she could provide food and clothes for her father.

심 봉사는 앞을 볼 수가 없었기 때문에 아무 일도 하지 못했습니다.

그래서 청이는 어려서부터 남의 집 일을 해 주고 음식을 얻어와 아버지를 공양했습니다.

마을 사람들은 입을 모아 부지런하고 착한 청이를 칭찬했습니다.

마을 아낙네들은 다투어 청이에게 바느질감을 맡겼습니다.

청이는 아버지에게 좋은 음식과 옷을 지어 드리기 위해 이른 아침부터 밤 늦게까지 열심히 일했습니다.

When Ch'ong was fifteen years old, something happened that changed her life forever.

She went to a village far from home in order to work. There was so much work to do, it was dark before she was able to leave for home.

It was very late at night and Blind Shim was very worried about Ch'ong. "Where can the poor child be?" he asked himself. Then he went outside to wait for her.

He took his cane and fumbled across the bridge that led to the village. But he stumbled and fell plop into the stream below.

"Save me! Save me!" he shouted as he splashed about in the water.

A Buddhist monk was passing by just at that moment. He ran to the stream and pulled Blind Shim out of the water.

심 청의 나이가 열다섯 살이 되던 해 어느 날이었습니다.

건너 마을로 일을 나갔던 청이는 일이 많아서 밤 늦게까지 집으로 돌아올 수 없었습니다.

심 봉사는 걱정이 되어 청이를 마중하러 나섰습니다.

지팡이를 짚고 더듬거리며 마을 앞 다리를 건너던 심 봉사는 발을 헛디뎌 그만 개천에 '풍덩' 빠지고 말았습니다.

"아이쿠, 사람 살려! 사람 살려!"

심 봉사는 허위적거리며 소리를 질렀습니다.

때마침 그 곳을 지나던 스님이 얼른 달려와 심 봉사를 건져 주었습니다.

"Thank you, thank you," Blind Shim said over and over, as the monk led him back home.

"If you give Buddha 300 bags of rice," said the monk, "you will be able to see again."

At this, Blind Shim perked up and he stopped saying, "Thank you, thank you." Instead, he exclaimed, "What's that you said? I could see again?" Blind Shim was so excited at the possibility of seeing again that he made a promise without thinking. "Oh, holy monk," he said, "I will. I will give you 300 bags of rice."

After the monk left, Blind Shim began to think about the promise that he had made. He began to worry.

심 봉사는 몇 번이고 고맙다는 인사를 되풀이했습니다.

스님은 심 봉사를 집으로 데려다 주었습니다.

"부처님께 쌀 삼백 석을 바치면 눈을 뜰 수 있지요."

심 봉사와 이야기를 나누던 스님은 이렇게 말했습니다.

"예! 눈을 뜰 수 있다구요?"

심 봉사는 귀가 번쩍 띄었습니다.

"스님, 쌀 삼백 석을 바치겠습니다."

심 봉사는 생각할 겨를도 없이 덜컥 약속을 해 버렸습니다.

스님이 돌아가고나자, 심 봉사는 걱정을 하기 시작했습니다.

"How can I keep such a promise?" he asked himself. "Ch'ong has a hard time just getting enough food for three small meals a day. How can she possibly get 300 bags of rice?"

When Ch'ong finally got home, she saw her father's worried look. "Father," she asked, "what happened today?"

Blind Shim told her how he worried about her, how he fell into the stream, and how the monk saved him. And he told her he promised to give the monk 300 bags of rice in order to see again.

Ch'ong tried to make her father feel better. "Don't worry," she said. "I will think of something."

"내가 어쩌다 그런 약속을 했을까? 하루 세끼 밥을 먹기도 어려운 살림인데……."

늦게 돌아온 청이는 아버지의 어두운 얼굴을 보고 걱정이 되어 여쭈어 보았습니다.

그러자 심 봉사는 청이가 걱정되어 집을 나섰던 일이며, 개천에 빠진 그를 스님이 구해 주었던 일, 다시 눈을 뜨기 위해 공양미 삼백 석을 스님에게 주기로 약속했던 일, 모두를 청이에게 이야기했습니다.

"아버지 제가 어떻게든 마련해 보겠어요. 너무 걱정하지 마세요."

청이는 아버지의 걱정을 덜어 주려고 이렇게 말했습니다.

For many days she thought about how she could ever get so many bags of rice. Then she heard that some sailors wanted to buy a young girl to sacrifice to the Dragon King so that they could make a safe journey.

Ch'ong went to the sailors and told them her sad story. She said she would sell herself to them for 300 bags of rice.

The sailors were very moved by her story, and very impressed by her goodheartedness. They told her, "Dear maiden, don't worry about your father any longer. We will give you the 300 bags of rice you need and we will also give your father rice to eat every day."

청이는 그렇게 많은 쌀을 어떻게 구해야 할지 여러 날을 곰곰히 생각해 보았습니다.

그러던 어느 날, 청이는 배를 타는 장사꾼들이 처녀를 사러 다닌다는 소문을 들었습니다.

청이는 장사꾼들을 찾아가서 딱한 사정을 이야기하고, 쌀 삼백 석에 자기 몸을 팔겠다고 했습니다.

장사꾼들은 아버지의 눈을 뜨게 하려는 청이의 고운 마음씨에 머리를 숙였습니다.

"아가씨, 이제 아버지 걱정은 하지 마시오. 쌀 삼백 석에다가 아버지가 먹고 살 수 있는 쌀을 더 드리겠소."
장사꾼들은 이렇게 약속을 했습니다.

15

She tried to comfort her weeping father, but she had to leave him to go far away with the sailors.

At the sea coast they boarded a big ship and set sail for China. When the ship reached the middle of the Indangsu Sea, a strong wind suddenly began to blow and high waves rocked the ship.

The frightened sailors prepared a table of food offerings for the Dragon King. They bowed toward the sea and prayed, crying out, "Please. Please. We beg you, great Dragon King. Spare us. Save us from this storm and let us cross the ocean."

Ch'ong stood at the front of the boat. She looked one last time in the direction of her home and then threw herself into the angry waves.

청이는 울부짖는 아버지를 남겨 두고 장사꾼들을 따라 먼 길을 떠났습니다.

바닷가에 닿은 청이는 중국으로 떠나는 큰 배를 탔습니다.

배가 '인당수' 라는 바다 가운데 이르자, 갑자기 사나운 바람이 불고 높은 파도가 일었습니다.

그러자 장사꾼들은 상을 차려 놓고 바다를 향해 엎드려 빌었습니다.

"비나이다. 비나이다. 용왕님께 비나이다. 저희들이 살아서 바다를 건너게 해 주십시오."

청이는 뱃머리에 서서 다시 한 번 고향 쪽을 되돌아 보고는 바다 속으로 풍덩 몸을 던졌습니다.

The sea suddenly became quiet. Relieved, but sad, the sailors sailed on.

Several days passed.

Ch'ong had been asleep for a long time. She woke up and stretched her arms. "Where am I ?" she asked herself.

She was in a beautiful room, the likes of which she had never seen before. Outside the windows, fish were swimming. A beautiful maiden came in and said, "Welcome to the Dragon Palace. The Dragon King brought you here when you sacrificed yourself to save the ship."

He knew how kindhearted Ch'ong was and how devoted she was to her father. So he put her inside the petals of a giant lotus flower and sent her back into the world.

바다는 잔잔해졌습니다.

그리고 며칠이 지났습니다.

오랫동안 잠에 빠져 있던 청이는 기지개를 켜며 일어났습니다.

"아니, 여기가 어딜까 ?"

청이는 처음 보는 아름다운 방에 와 있었습니다. 창 밖에는 물고기들이 헤엄치고 있었습니다.

그 때 고운 여자 한 사람이 와서 청이에게 말했습니다.

"청이 아가씨, 이곳은 바다 속의 용궁입니다. 용왕님께서 아가씨를 이곳으로 데려오게 하셨지요."

용왕님은 효성이 지극한 청이를 커다란 연꽃 봉오리 속에 넣어 다시 세상으로 나가게 해 주었습니다.

Ch'ong slept peacefully inside the flower, gently rocking back and forth on the waves of the ocean.

Some fishermen saw the giant flower floating in the sea. "Oh!" they exclaimed, "such a beautiful and magnificent flower must have been sent from the Dragon King." They pulled the lotus flower into their boat and took it to their king.

The king also thought the huge lotus was a great wonder.

And then, all at once, the petals of the great lotus began to slowly open.

연꽃 속에 들어간 청이는 바다 위로 두둥실 떠 올랐습니다.

바다에서 고기를 잡던 어부들이 청이가 들어 있는 연꽃을 보았습니다.

"이렇게 크고 아름다운 연꽃은 용왕님이 보내신 것이 틀림없어."

어부들은 연꽃을 배에 싣고 가 임금님께 바쳤습니다.

임금님도 커다란 연꽃을 몹시 신기하게 여겼습니다.

그 때 연꽃 봉오리가 사르르 벌어졌습니다.

"What's this? Someone is coming out of the flower!"
"아니! 연꽃에셔 사람이 나오다니……."

In the middle of the lotus flower stood beautiful Ch'ong. Every-one in the palace was very surprised, the king most of all. The king thought that the lotus maiden was so lovely that he asked her to become his queen.

Even after Ch'ong became the queen, she still thought often about her poor blind father. At such times she became unbearably sad.

One day, when she was thinking of her home in the land by the Yellow Sea, the king asked her what was wrong. "If something is troubling you," he said, "please tell me." So Ch'ong told him all about her life and about her father, Blind Shim.

연꽃 속에는 아름다운 청이가 서 있었습니다.

대궐 안에 있던 사람들은 모두 깜짝 놀랐습니다.

임금님은 아름다운 청이를 왕비로 맞아들였습니다.

그러나 왕비가 된 청이는 홀로 계신 아버지를 생각하며 늘 슬픔에 잠겨 있었습니다.

하루는 임금님이 청이에게 말했습니다.

"걱정이 있으면 모두 이야기해 보시오."

그러자 청이는 지나간 이야기를 하기 시작했습니다.

After hearing Ch'ong's sad story, the king slapped his knee and said, "I have it! We will hold a grand feast for all the blind people in the land. That way, we will be able to find your father."

The feast was held in the palace over many days. Every day, countless blind men were brought to the palace where they ate delicious food and were entertained by the court musicians. Queen Ch'ong looked for her father every day. She looked and looked, but he didn't come.

The feast was almost over, and Ch'ong had almost given up hope, when an old blind man in very ragged clothes stumbled in.

이야기를 다 듣고 난 임금님은 무릎을 탁 쳤습니다.

"온 나라 안에 있는 장님들을 불러 모아 잔치를 베풀어 줍시다. 그러면 아버지를 찾을 수 있을 거요."

그 날부터 대궐에서는 커다란 잔치가 베풀어졌습니다.

수많은 장님들이 대궐로 몰려들어와 맛있는 음식을 먹으며 즐겁게 놀았습니다.

청이는 이제나저제나 아버지가 오시기를 애타게 기다렸습니다.

잔치가 다 끝나갈 무렵, 허름한 차림을 한 심 봉사가 더듬거리며 대궐 안으로 들어왔습니다.

"Father!" cried out the beautiful queen and she ran to the old man and hugged him.

Blind Shim's face was clouded in confusion. "Who is this girl who calls me father?" he asked. When people told him it was the queen, he became even more confused.

"Father, it's me. Your daughter, Ch'ong," she said.

Her father was so surprised that his eyes opened in amazement. And he could see!

Blind Shim was not blind any more. He shouted, "Oh! I see you at last! I see my beautiful daughter at last!"

Shim Ch'ong and her father hugged each other tightly and cried tears of happiness.

Ceremony 대상미 이제, 데이, 세부

"아버지!"
청이는 아버지를 '와락' 껴안았습니다.
심 봉사는 어리둥절하여 물었습니다.
"누구신데 나를 아버지라고 부르는 거요?"
사람들이 심 봉사에게 그녀가 왕비라고 말해 주자, 심 봉사는 더욱 어리둥절해졌습니다.

"아버지, 저예요. 딸 청이에요."
"뭐라고, 내 딸 청이라고? 네가 살아있었다니……, 어디 좀 보자."
심 봉사는 눈을 번쩍 떴습니다.
"아! 보이는구나. 내 딸 청이가 보이는구나!"
심 봉사는 청이를 얼싸안고 기쁨의 눈물을 흘렸습니다.

The Little Frog Who Never Listened

In a small pond there lived Mother Frog and her son Little Frog. Little Frog was like very many human boys and girls. He never listened to what his Mother told him. If Mother Frog said, "You must play in the lower village today because they say that many fierce animals are hunting in the upper village," then, of course, Little Frog playfully hopped up to the upper village.

말 안 듣는 청개구리

조그만 연못에 엄마청개구리와 아들 청개구리가 살고 있었습니다.

아들청개구리는 엄마의 말을 듣지 않는 말썽꾸러기였습니다.

"얘야, 오늘은 아랫동네에 가서 놀아라. 윗동네에는 무서운 짐승들이 많이 온단다."

엄마청개구리가 이렇게 말하면, 아들청개구리는 윗동네로 폴짝폴짝 뛰어갔습니다.

Whatever Mother Frog told her son to do, he did the very opposite.   If Mother Frog told Little Frog to play in the mountains, he played at the edge of the pond.   If Mother Frog sent him on an errand, he went swimming.

"How can I break my son of his bad habit?" Mother Frog wondered. She breathed out a long, sad sigh.

One day, Mother Frog called her son. After much trouble she finally got him to sit still. She told him, "Child, you still cannot croak properly. You must learn. So pay attention and do as I do."

아들청개구리는 엄마가 시키는 것은 무엇이든 거꾸로 했습니다.

엄마청개구리가 산에 가서 놀라고 하면 아들 청개구리는 물가에 가서 놀았습니다.

엄마청개구리가 심부름을 시키면 아들청개구리는 수영을 하러갔습니다.

'어떻게 하면 저 아이의 나쁜 버릇을 고칠 수 있을까?'

엄마청개구리는 한숨을 '푸욱' 쉬며 슬퍼했습니다.

하루는 엄마청개구리가 아들청개구리를 불러 앉히고 말했습니다.

"애야, 넌 우는 소리가 아직 서투르구나. 엄마가 잘 가르쳐 줄테니 그대로 따라해 보아라."

Then Mother Frog croaked in a very beautiful bass voice, "Ri-but, ribut, ribut." Little Frog butted in rudely. "Oh, Mother, I can do that. Just listen." And he blurted out in a very high, unfroglike voice, "Ut-rib, ut-rib, ut-rib."

Mother Frog looked up at the sky and beat her chest. But Little Frog just laughed and laughed. "Hee, hee. It's great fun to play tricks on Mother."

And he hopped away singing, "Ut-rib, ut-rib, ut-rib."

엄마청개구리는 고운 목소리로 '개굴 개굴개굴' 울었습니다.

"알았어요. 엄마."

아들청개구리는 퉁명스럽게 대답을 하고 목청을 돋구어 울었습니다.

"굴개 굴개 굴개 굴개……."

엄마청개구리는 너무 답답해서 가슴을 쳤습니다.

"히히, 난 엄마가 화난 모습이 재미 있어요."

아들청개구리는 랄라랄라 노래를 부르며 밖으로 뛰어나갔습니다.

Mother Frog was so upset that she became sick. She lay on her lily pad, groaning, "Oh, oh! I feel very sick! Oh, oh!"

She called her son to her and said, "My child, please listen to me very carefully this time. If I die, please don't bury me in the mountains. Bury me by the water's edge."

Mother Frog really wanted to be buried in the mountains, but she told her son to bury her by the water's edge because he always did the opposite of what he was told.

아들 때문에 속을 썩이던 엄마청개구리는 병이 나고 말았습니다.

"아이고, 아파라. 아이고."

엄마청개구리는 자리에 누워 끙끙 앓았습니다.

어느 날, 엄마청개구리는 아들청개구리를 불러 말했습니다.

"얘야, 내가 죽거들랑 산에 묻지 말고 냇가에 묻어다오."

엄마청개구리는 이렇게 말을 해야만 아들청개구리가 산에 묻어줄 것이라고 생각했습니다.

In a few days, poor Mother Frog died. Little Frog cried and cried. "It's all my fault. Forgive me, Mother."

He felt very bad about the way he had treated his mother. "I always did the opposite of what I was told because I thought it was fun to tease Mother. But now, I should at least listen to her last request." So Little Frog took his mother's body and carefully buried it at the water's edge.

엄마청개구리는 얼마 지나지 않아 세상을 뜨고 말았습니다.

아들청개구리는 엉엉 슬피 울었습니다.

"나 때문에 엄마가 죽었구나. 용서해 주세요, 엄마. 엉엉……."

아들청개구리는 그제서야 자기의 잘못을 뉘우쳤습니다.

'지금까지 엄마 속만 썩였구나. 엄마의 마지막 부탁만은 들어 드려야지.'

아들청개구리는 죽은 엄마를 냇가에 고이고이 묻었습니다.

The reason Mother Frog wanted to be buried in the mountains was that she knew her body would be swept away by highwater if she were buried by the pond.

A few days later, there was a big rainstorm. Little Frog couldn't sleep, so he stood beside the grave crying, "Ribut, ribut, ribut. If the stream gets any higher, the water will float Mamma away! What can I do? Ribut, ribut, ribut."

The more it rained, the more Little Frog hopped around, crying, "Rain, rain, please stop. If it keeps raining, Mamma's going to float away forever! Ribut, ribut, ribut."

And so, even today, whenever it rains, little frogs hop around and cry, "Ribut, ribut, ribut."

엄마청개구리가 죽은 뒤에 큰 비가 내렸습니다.

아들청개구리는 잠 한숨 못 자고 개굴개굴 울면서 엄마의 무덤을 지켰습니다.

"냇물이 넘쳐서 엄마 무덤이 떠내려 가면 어쩌나……. 개굴 개굴 개굴 ……."

비가 오는 날이면 아들청개구리는 발을 동동 구르며 울었습니다.

"비야 비야, 오지 말아라. 우리 엄마 떠내려 간단다. 개굴 개굴 개굴 개굴 ……."

그 뒤로 청개구리들은 비만 오면 개굴개굴 울게 되었습니다.

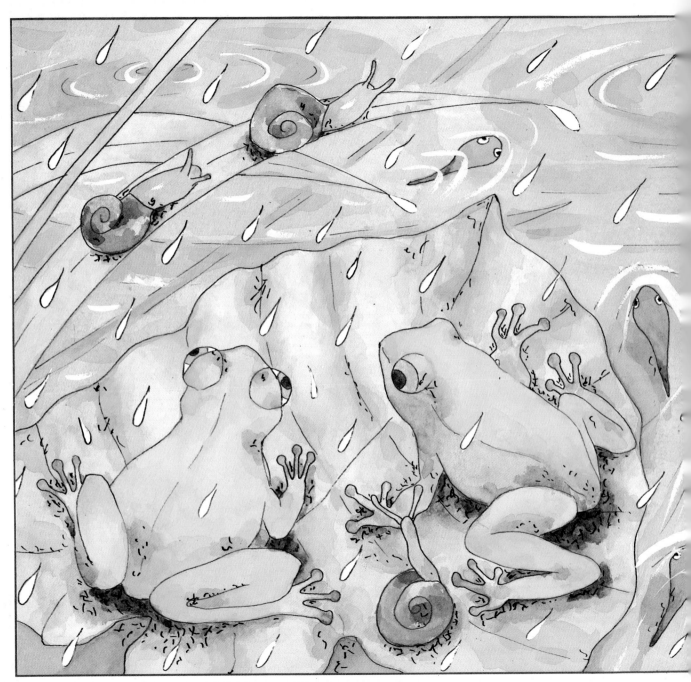

45